CW00701310

THE BEATLES
Playalong *for* Clarinet

WISE PUBLICATIONS
London/New York/Paris/Sydney/Copenhagen/Madrid

Clarinet Fingering Chart

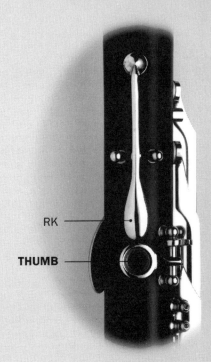

RK

THUMB

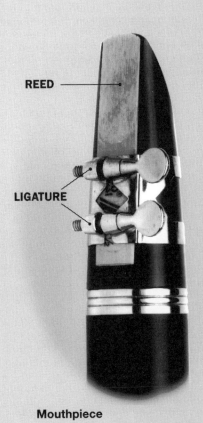

REED

LIGATURE

Mouthpiece

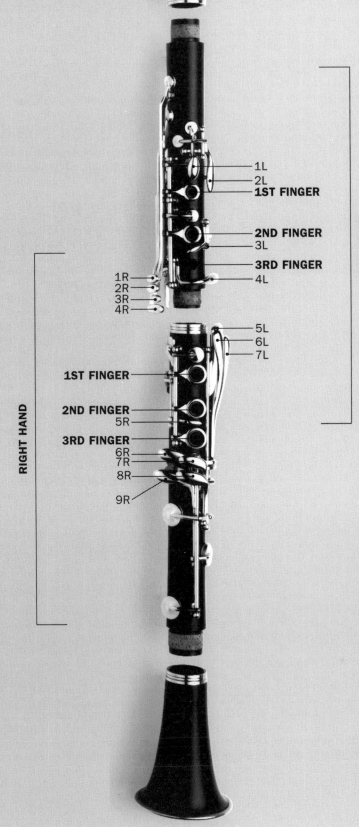

1L
2L
1ST FINGER

2ND FINGER
3L

3RD FINGER

1R
2R
3R
4R

4L

LEFT HAND

5L
6L
7L

1ST FINGER

2ND FINGER
5R

3RD FINGER

6R
7R
8R

9R

RIGHT HAND

Transposition

E♭ clarinet sounds a minor third above
the written pitch. Rule: **Written C sounds E♭**

Written:

Sounds:

B♭ clarinet sounds a major second below
the written pitch. Rule: **Written C sounds B♭**

Written:

Sounds:

E♭ alto clarinet sounds a major sixth below
the written pitch. Rule: **Written C sounds E♭**

Written:

Sounds:

B♭ bass clarinet sounds a major ninth below
the written pitch. Rule: **Written C sounds B♭**

Written:

Sounds:

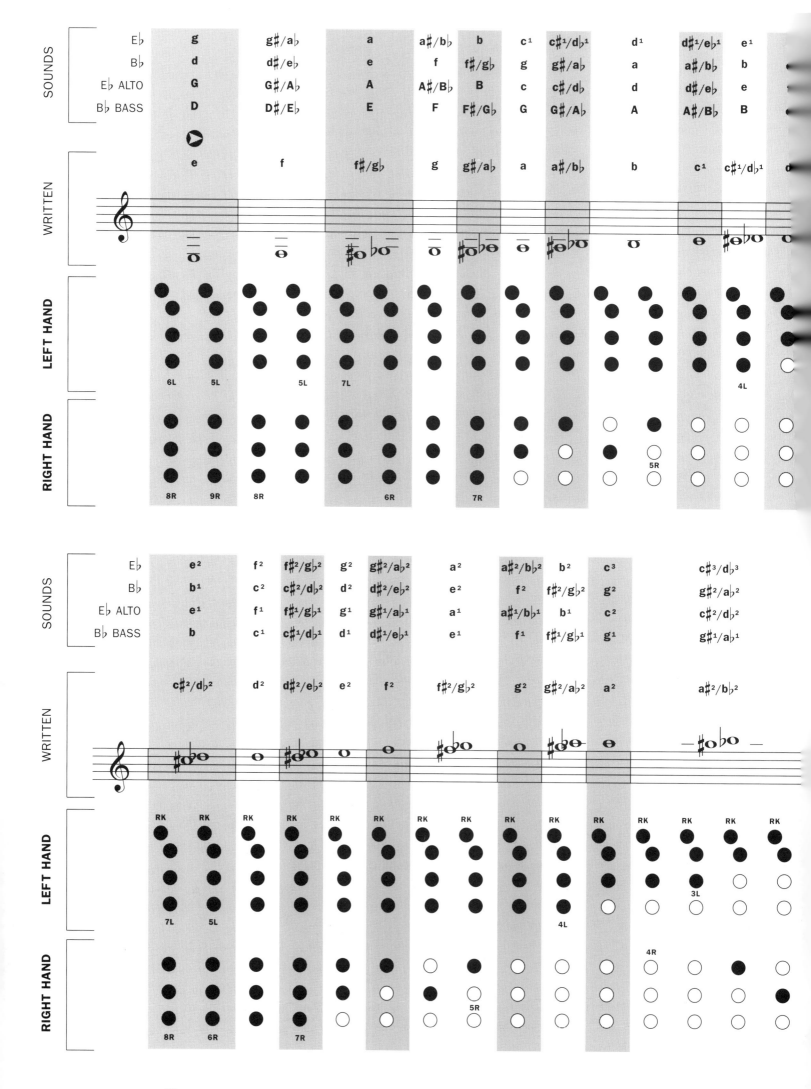

Indicates the lower limit of the best playing range for E♭, B♭, E♭ Alto and B♭ Bass Clarinets

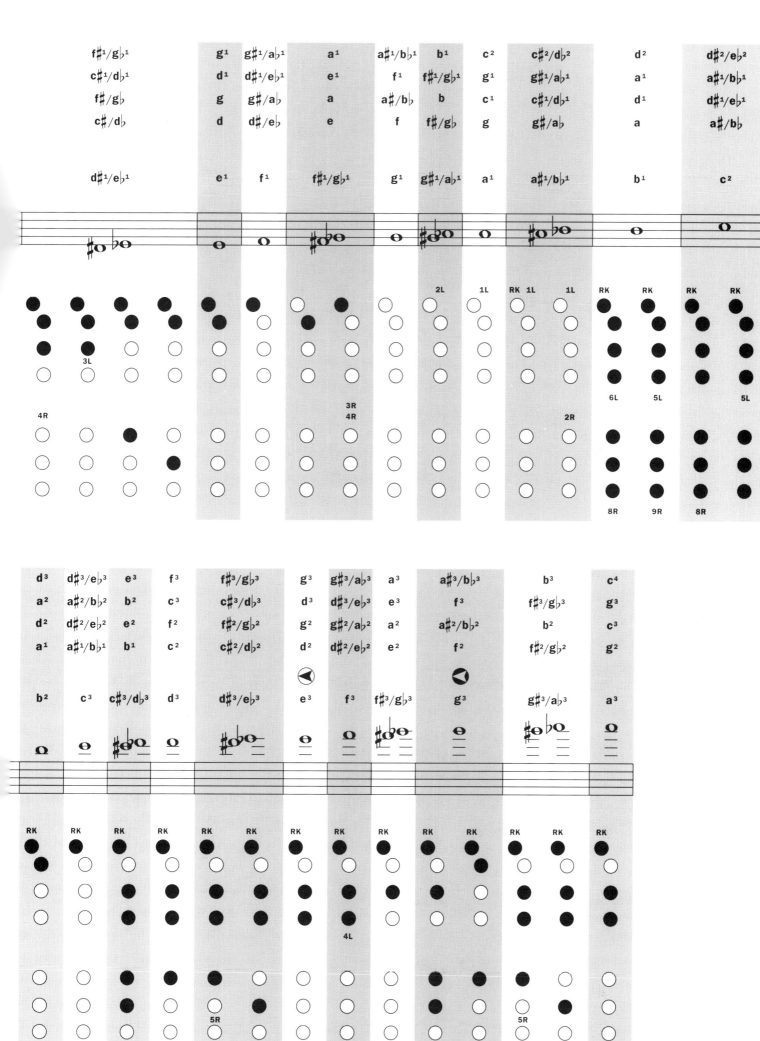

Indicates the upper limit of the best playing range for E♭ and B♭ Clarinets   Indicates the upper limit of the best playing range for E♭ Alto and B♭ Bass Clarinets

Here, There And Everywhere

Words & Music by John Lennon & Paul McCartney

Moderately Slow

Hey Jude

Words & Music by John Lennon & Paul McCartney

Slowly

9

Repeat and fade

All You Need Is Love

Words & Music by John Lennon & Paul McCartney

Moderately

Repeat and fade

Michelle

Words & Music by John Lennon & Paul McCartney

Moderately

Penny Lane

Words & Music by John Lennon & Paul McCartney

Moderately

She's Leaving Home

Words & Music by John Lennon & Paul McCartney

Moderately

mp

mf

poco rall.

dim.

2

mp

Lady Madonna

Words & Music by John Lennon & Paul McCartney

Rhythmically

She Loves You

Words & Music by John Lennon & Paul McCartney

Bright Tempo

When I'm Sixty Four

Words & Music by John Lennon & Paul McCartney

Rhythmically

Yesterday

Words & Music by John Lennon & Paul McCartney

Moderately

espress.

rall.

dim.

Music Sales Limited
8/9 Frith Street, London W1V 5TZ, England.
Music Sales Pty Limited
120 Rothschild Avenue, Rosebery, NSW 2018, Australia.

Order No. NO90682
ISBN 0-7119-7342-3
This book © Copyright 1999 by Wise Publications.

Book design by Michael Bell Design.
Music arranged by Paul Honey.
Music processed by Enigma Music Production Services.
Cover photography by George Taylor.
Printed in the United Kingdom by Page Bros., Norwich, Norfolk.

CD produced by Paul Honey.
Instrumental solos by John Whelan.
All guitars by Arthur Dick.
Engineered by Kester Sims.

Your Guarantee of Quality:
As publishers, we strive to produce every book to
the highest commercial standards.
The music has been freshly engraved and the book has been
carefully designed to minimise awkward page turns and
to make playing from it a real pleasure.
Particular care has been given to specifying acid-free, neutral-sized
paper made from pulps which have not been elemental chlorine bleached.
This pulp is from farmed sustainable forests and was
produced with special regard for the environment.
Throughout, the printing and binding have been planned to
ensure a sturdy, attractive publication which should give years of enjoyment.
If your copy fails to meet our high standards,
please inform us and we will gladly replace it.

Music Sales' complete catalogue describes thousands of
titles and is available in full colour sections by subject,
direct from Music Sales Limited.
Please state your areas of interest and send a
cheque/postal order for £1.50 for postage to:
Music Sales Limited, Newmarket Road, Bury St. Edmunds, Suffolk IP33 3YB.